THE BOUDICA WITHIN

C000263898

To my mother Mireille and to my brother Michael

To Bob Allen MD, my mentor and friend

THE BOUDICA WITHIN

*The extraordinary journey of women
after breast cancer and reconstruction*

Elaine Sassoon

Photography
Andrea O'Hare

With the participation of
Chrystèle Ganivet and Neil Watson

The Erskine Press
2007

THE BOUDICA WITHIN

*The extraordinary journey of women
after breast cancer and reconstruction*

Elaine Sassoon

Photography Andrea O'Hare

With the participation of
Chrystèle Ganivet and Neil Watson

First published in 2007 *by
The Erskine Press, The White House, Eccles, Norwich NR16 2PB*
www.erskine-press.com

ISBN 978-1-85297-097-0

Text and illustrations © Elaine Sassoon 2007

The moral right of the author has been asserted

A CIP catalogue record of this book is available from the British Library

No part of this book may be reproduced in any form,
by printing, photocopying or by any other means without
the prior written permission of the Publisher

*Typeset by Waveney Typesetters, Wymondham, Norfolk
Printed and bound in England at
The University Press, Cambridge*

INTRODUCTION

I had gone to meet one of the breast surgeons to plan my job as the new Consultant Plastic Surgeon charged with setting up a formal breast reconstruction service for Norfolk, which would include immediate reconstruction.

> 'Women in Norfolk don't want a breast. They are down-to-earth farmers, they have better things to think about, so you are not needed.

I ignored the comment and persevered, and in the 10 years I have spent looking after my Norfolk breast reconstruction patients I have been constantly impressed by their fortitude, resilience and sense of humour. I observed their change from victims to extraordinary women who discovered inner strengths they never knew they possessed. They were no longer cancer survivors, but appeared to soar, altered for the better by the terrible experiences they had undergone, often full of joy or possessing a new calmness from finding their own pathway.

I wanted to pay tribute to this transformation and to the natural spirit that surfaces in times of adversity. I felt privileged to have witnessed this and wanted to celebrate it. I did not know how. Then three years ago I was shown the wonderful book *Reconstructing Aphrodite* (Pub. Verve Editions, USA) by the photographer Terry Lorant. I was inspired to write about some of my own patients.

Why the name THE BOUDICA WITHIN?

Boudica means 'Bringer of Victory'. She was a local woman to Norfolk, leader of the Iceni at around 40AD; an ordinary woman who through circumstances outside of her control, became extraordinary. I felt that she represented the courage and spirit I witness daily.

The women involved in this book are all patients of mine, all motivated by the desire to help others diagnosed with breast cancer. They have all responded positively to my request and been prepared to reveal themselves in this book. We hoped particularly to demonstrate to women who have just been given the terrible diagnosis of cancer, and who are faced with the prospect of mutilating surgery and debilitating treatment, that a few months hence, they can feel whole, gorgeous and strong again. We wanted to show this via photographs, but also by letting their voices be heard through their stories. I hope that our purpose has been achieved. Where I have used specific surgical or anatomical terms I have explained them in the glossary on page 124. For technical details of the operations performed see the index on pages 130–131.

We plastic surgeons are incredibly competitive and very sensitive to the scrutiny of our peers. It would have been so easy to select only the best results and air-brush any imperfections. But that would have betrayed the purpose of the book. So I chose real women, some young, some older, some whose operations were a real struggle for me, some whom I had not seen for years and others with still immature red scars.

For all these extraordinary women, this is their book.

June 2007   Elaine Sassoon

BOUDICA

Boudica (or Boudicca) was queen of the Iceni of present day East Anglia, and leader of the union of British Tribes who in AD 60 rebelled against the oppressive Gaius Suetonius Paullinus, then Roman Governor of Britannia.

Following the death of her husband Prasutagus, client king of the Iceni tribe, all her possessions were seized by Rome. When she objected, her family was disinherited, her daughters raped and she was stripped and flogged.

Boudica found the inner strength to lead the Iceni, along with other tribes, in revolt. They destroyed Camulodunum (Colchester), now a settlement for veteran Roman soldiers and the site of a temple to the former emperor Claudius, the Roman emperor who completed the conquest of Britain. They also routed a Roman legion sent to relieve the soldiers. Then they ransacked St Albans.

ACKNOWLEDGEMENTS

After planning and thinking of this book for three years, everything suddenly came together and in only six months the idea became reality.

This certainly would never have been the case without my friend Chrystèle. I was progressing on the project, slowly and intermittently, as and when my job as a consultant plastic surgeon in a teaching hospital allowed. I had a publisher. I knew the format I wanted and I had a list of 100 patients whom I could call. I envisaged mainly outdoor photographs and I knew the type of photography needed: powerful and sexy. I did not know how to find the photographer and I did not have the time to do so. Chrystèle took charge and interviewed several before approaching my patient Andrea O'Hare whom I felt it would have been intrusive and possibly unethical for me personally to recruit. Every time I found myself distracted by the pressing concerns of running both a busy NHS department and private practice she was on the phone, pushing me to speak to this person, write that chapter etc. She shamed me with her endless energy and helped me considerably in collecting and editing the patient stories and reviewing our notes with her husband Neil. So this book is their baby as well. It has likewise become that of all the women featured, whose voices are heard in these pages.

Andrea of course carried the project to another dimension through her beautiful photography. She knew instinctively what I wanted – no mean feat!

My friends Liz and Debbie gave me much needed encouragement in the early days when the Boudica project was just a concept. Everyone has been so positive it has been a pleasure as well as a privilege to work with them. Some women travelled a long way to be photographed as 'they wouldn't have missed it for the world'. I understand that many found it a very moving and liberating experience.

I want to express my special thanks to Bronwen. She introduced me to Jane and Hugh Alston and to Susan Bullock. Jane and Hugh generously allowed us to set up base and photograph at Bradfield Hall Farm near Trunch in North Norfolk for two days, and Susan opened up her beautiful garden in nearby Swafield for our use. So thanks to them too. I am also particularly beholden to Caroline and Roger Combe for graciously giving us the full run of Bayfield Hall and its grounds.

The delightful Hannah Lindsay cannot go unmentioned, as she worked tirelessly and enthusiastically for three days as facial makeup artist for the subjects of the book.

James Ruddy, ex-deputy editor of the *Eastern Daily Press*, first put me in touch with my publisher Cris de Boos a year and a half ago, and has been a great source of advice since. And thanks to Cris of course for taking up this project.

My long-term friend Robert Scully rode to my rescue as usual when I discovered the importance of copyright, printing presses, distribution etc., and I worried about not learning fast enough. His friend Pedro Prá-Lopez generously shared his experience and knowledge of design.

I would like to thank the Medical Illustration department of the Norfolk and Norwich University Hospital for allowing me to use their photographs for the Reconstruction Information section.

Indirectly, all the members of the plastic surgery department at the Norfolk and Norwich University Hospital and BUPA Norwich have played a part in the creation of this book by caring for these women and by helping them in their recovery. I am proud to be a member of a very professional team. This includes my consultant colleagues who shared their experience generously and gave their advice in the early days. The close working relationship I have with my delightful colleague Richard Haywood has allowed us to really move forward with the provision of a comprehensive breast reconstructive service for our part of East Anglia. I must mention Ruth Harcourt, our indispensable reconstruction nurse. I could never forget my wonderful secretaries Lorraine Horan and Pauline Osborne, who cheerfully remind me that without them, nothing would ever function.

My East Grinstead consultant colleague and friend Roger Smith checked and validated the reconstruction information section for me, and I am beholden to Venkat Ramakrishnan, my colleague and friend from Chelmsford, for all his support.

Finally, but never least, Penny Morgan, Director of International Branches, and Elin (now Mrs Gillard), Territory manager of Mentor Medical Systems Ltd., UK never doubted that the project was possible. Their support, both financial and practical, has been central to the success of THE BOUDICA WITHIN. I am all the more grateful and impressed because they know that I am a strong advocate of free perforator flap reconstructions.

THE STORIES

I'm proud of who I am, I just hadn't realised it!

It was Friday afternoon and the end of another long week. I wished my class of 10 year olds a good weekend and told them that I'd see them again on Monday afternoon as I had a hospital appointment in the morning. I never taught them again.

I approached my first routine mammogram without too much worry. I was surprised however when the examination of my right breast was so much more painful than the other. It left me with a feeling of being badly bruised and sore, which would not go away. After two visits to my GP and a course of antibiotics I was finally referred to the breast clinic. The referral arrived at the same time as my recall from the mammogram.

Bad news piled onto bad news. My anticipated lumpectomy became a mastectomy, then the biopsy of my lymph node wasn't clear. A whirlwind of operations, tests, treatments with terrible side effects saw me hit the floor. I lost my hair, nails and my ability to taste and enjoy food; at times I wondered if it was worth going on. But my family were superb and helped me through.

I found living without a breast so much more difficult than I imagined. More than just taking the breast, the surgery changed the contours of my whole upper body. I began disguising my deformity with layers and scarves and clothes I would never have dreamt of wearing before. I suffered humiliations and anguish. One insensitive assistant in a lingerie boutique announced to the whole shop that I was buying a mastectomy bra. On another occasion my daughter found me in tears because I was unable to find a suitable swimming costume for my holiday.

The decision to have reconstruction was an easy one. The result is not perfect, I didn't expect it to be; but it is better than I could have hoped for and I am delighted with it. Yet what has surprised a lot of people most, my husband and myself included, is the effect that it has had on my confidence. A friend recently commented how I dress and move with far greater confidence, I wear brighter colours and more 'glitz' as if I am proud of who I am. And yes I am. I just hadn't ever realised it.

Barbara

If you've got it, flaunt it

It would have taken a lot longer for my breast cancer to be diagnosed had I not recently taken up yoga. During one class I was practicing the 'plough' pose, with my back raised off the floor and my legs behind my head. I remember thinking how squashed my breasts were, and the next day I noticed a pin-prick of blood on my sports bra. I put it back on and realised that the spot lined up perfectly with my nipple.

I went to my GP to have it checked out. She couldn't detect a lump, but sent me to a Breast Clinic 'just in case'. I was diagnosed with early stage breast cancer following that visit.

I chose not to have an immediate reconstruction with my mastectomy as I wanted more time to research my options. Fifteen months later I travelled over 100 miles from my home to have my breast rebuilt. Of course there were disadvantages with this, but they were outweighed by the advantages. My husband accompanied me on all my appointments so we turned them into treats, often staying overnight in a nice hotel, exploring the countryside or stopping for a meal on the way home.

Having breast cancer has certainly changed my life but there have been many positive outcomes. It has made me realise how wonderfully supportive my family and friends are and how lucky I am to have them. I have met lots of lovely people and have noticed how positive and happy many fellow breast cancer survivors are. I have stopped worrying about the future and enjoy the present far more than before.

The most surprising thing is that I was never very confident with my body and would not have dreamed of showing it off. Even though I am still very much a work in progress, having had further surgery only three weeks before the photo shoot, I did not hesitate to take part. After living without a breast for over a year I am just so delighted to have one again that I don't care who sees it!

It is wonderful to wear low cut clothes again. The success of the operation was brought home to me recently whilst shopping for an evening dress with my sister-in-law. I tried on a lovely gown with a very plunging neckline. I asked her if she thought it was too low cut and she replied 'No, if you've got it, flaunt it.' As I was standing there exposing vast amounts of cleavage, the shop assistant added 'Yes, some people would pay a lot of money to have ones like yours.' I just smiled!

Lynda

I wasn't given a choice, just take it or leave it, so I left it

I wasn't really interested in reconstruction at first. I had endured a lumpectomy with a wide excision, followed by radiotherapy and wasn't prepared for any more operations. I was 35, in a stable marriage with a four-year old son, Jacob. Reconstruction really didn't seem that important at the time. I was offered it, but I wasn't given a choice of procedures, just take it or leave it, so I left it.

I certainly didn't feel as attractive as I had done before the operation, but life fell back into a routine. I would still go swimming for example, although I did feel a little uncomfortable undressing with my stick-on prosthesis. Sometimes I even found it difficult letting my husband touch me there. But he was very supportive, our relationship was strong and after five years we had a beautiful daughter, Lily. She was the best thing that could possibly have happened following my illness.

Two years later my husband was gone and I fell into depression. I had lost all of my self-esteem and hated my body. I didn't love myself and so I could never imagine a man wanting to love me either. I needed counselling and the support of a good friend to help me to regain my strength and rediscover my identity. I have to say that this was a slow process, but in time I started to rebuild my confidence and focus more on myself.

Twelve months on I met Andrew, now my partner, and thanks to my counselling I was able to be open and honest with him about my body. Even so, I wasn't comfortable enough to actually show him my breast and he respected that. As our relationship developed, sharing my body with him proved difficult at first and I would always keep a top on even during lovemaking.

Soon, with my new-found confidence, I began to think more about what I wanted. I had a friend who had had reconstruction and after talking with her I decided that I was now ready to consider this also.

One year on and my life has certainly changed. I love my body and particularly my new bust. I thought I might be self conscious, but I felt that it was part of me immediately. My confidence is high and I am very happy. I can't in all honesty attribute this just to my reconstruction, but it has certainly played a significant contribution. I have progressed in my career and now work as a sexual health adviser within the NHS. My journey, albeit rough at times has undoubtedly helped me in this role where life experience is crucial.

Mel

Ah Mrs Jones, nature was not so kind. We can do much better than this

I had been to visit my friend Hazel in the hospice and I knew that her end was near and I would never see her again. She had been so cheerful, no doubt helped by morphine and gin & tonic. My heart was breaking. I had lost my mother to breast cancer at 42 and now a dear friend was going too. That evening, feeling low, I decided on a hot bath and early night. As I stretched to pick up some bubble bath I caught sight of my left breast in the mirror. The nightmare I had dreaded began.

I was to undergo a double mastectomy and quite frankly didn't really give a damn about reconstruction. I had never particularly liked my breasts, they were small and had already caused me quite a lot of problems, with benign tumours and severe mastitis; for me, they were time-bombs waiting to detonate. But I dutifully attended my meeting with the plastic surgeon of which I have very little recollection, except her commenting: 'Ah, Mrs Jones, nature was not so kind. We can do much better than this'.

As my treatment progressed my husband of 35 years was unable to cope and moved on. My cocker spaniel and horse gave me the company I so needed when I was just too ill to bother with people. Animals, unlike people, live in the moment; it was a lesson I needed to learn and they were superb teachers.

When I finally decided on reconstruction several girlfriends became worried and tried to talk me out of it; they thought I had gone through enough. But I wasn't coping with the falsies, my marriage was failing and I felt so unwomanly. I won't pretend it was easy but after the cancer treatment it was such a positive step: constructive not destructive.

So it was that I woke up in the hospital to hear that it had gone well, the nurses came around every half hour to listen for a pulse in each breast, to make sure that they had 'taken'. A strange thing started to happen. I began to like my breasts. They were my babies; they had a pulse, were alive and needed loving and cosseting. They didn't save my marriage but they did give me back my confidence and changed the way I felt about myself.

Bronwen

Never, never miss your mammography appointment

I thought it would be nice to be photographed with some of the items that I wore on my remarriage a year ago in May 2006. A very happy day with a wonderful man who has said he sees me as a beautiful woman who has had a breast reconstruction.

Back in the year 2000 life was certainly not running smoothly for me. After many years of suffering I had decided once and for all that I couldn't carry on living with my husband and started divorce proceedings. One morning, in the middle of this turmoil, a letter dropped through the door calling me in for my routine mammogram. I was tired emotionally and physically and was in no mood to go for this examination. In the end, reluctantly, I decided to attend.

At the time I received the results I was living alone. I was shattered by this additional trauma in my life and found it almost impossible to function. Life was dragging me along, I was in a daze and lacking concentration, something had to give. That's the time that I decided to put the divorce on hold. My husband moved back in and his attitude changed, but it was short lived.

After my mastectomy and reconstruction I began to feel stronger psychologically and completed my divorce. All I wanted now was some time for myself, filled only with peace and tranquillity. I certainly wasn't looking for another man; I had had enough of marriage for one lifetime thank you.

I went back to work full time. After being a florist, I became a reminiscence tutor with the elderly: a therapeutic job where I help isolated and lonely people, people who are in the place that I once was.

Then through friends I met Basil. He is a lovely man who I discovered has twice lost wives to this dreadful disease, once to breast cancer and then again to leukaemia. I have always tried to be straight and honest so after a couple of social dates and before the relationship developed I told him about me. I wanted to give him the opportunity to walk away; I didn't want to put him in a similar situation again. But he stayed and I am so glad he did: we have just celebrated our first wedding anniversary.

I would not be here, happy, married and content but for one decision I made, to go for my mammogram. So if there is one message I want to get across to all women it is never, never miss your mammography appointment regardless of your personal circumstances, you may not get a second chance.

Christine

I began to pull myself together; you either sink or swim in the end

Cancer is such a loaded word; it carries with it darkness, finality. So when I was diagnosed with breast cancer I simply fell apart and wrote myself off completely. I became haunted by black thoughts and was scared that I would die. I lost interest in everything and immediately put my business and house up for sale. I just couldn't conceive working my butt off only to find that I wouldn't be around to benefit from it.

Even survival did not seem such a great option. For me my breasts and my femininity are one; when a woman loses them it's no different to a man losing his privates. As a consequence I told my husband that he should leave me. I really believed that I would no longer be woman enough for him. My husband did his best to reassure me. He told me that he didn't care about my breasts, it was me that he wanted.

My treatment was long and made all the more difficult because my husband became ill during this time and was admitted to a clinic. I had to go through surgery alone.

I didn't really think about the procedure or the consequences. I was led through the whole thing like a lamb to the slaughter; a zombie, not able to see beyond it. Then during the chemotherapy I lost my precious long, blond hair. After everything else that seemed a devastating blow, stripping me of my last vestige of femininity. Even with a wig I felt very self-conscious and unwomanly.

Gradually, over a period of time I began to pull myself together. I guess you either sink or swim in the end.

I am now a far stronger person. I am back running my business and refuse to suffer fools gladly. People with petty complaints and trivial problems no longer entertain me. Life has certainly picked up: we are taking more holidays and living life spontaneously.

As for my breasts, they are now completed and better than I imagined they would be. My concerns about my femininity and desirability have vanished. Yes, you can recover both of these through reconstruction.

Katherine

I've never felt like I've lost a breast, only that mine has been worked on

I'm 50 years old and work as a receptionist in a medical centre in Norfolk, so I have always been aware of breast cancer and check myself regularly. Two years ago I noticed some discharge from my nipple and mentioned this to a colleague who advised me to have it checked just for my own peace of mind. I went to my GP who, having found nothing, still referred me to the breast clinic as there is a history of breast cancer in my family.

I was very blasé about it and despite having a mammogram and biopsy, decided to just pop out from work to pick up the results and go back. As I lay in a side room the consultant broke the bad news to me very gently. The first thought that struck me was that I was crying, and if I didn't sit up the tears would run into my ears. The realisation of what he had said only came later.

I think my overwhelming feeling is that I am lucky. Not just because I'm alive and well, but for a number of reasons.

Both my aunt and my cousin had previously suffered from breast cancer. My cousin had reconstruction by the same surgeon a week before me, and we even had the same bed in the same ward. Consequently I had a strong support network with my family at the core.

Even though I've had radical surgery I haven't had to undergo the harsh treatment and side effects that others have been through; that is something that I remain thankful for. Actually I've never even felt like I've lost a breast, only that mine has been worked on. This notion is reinforced because the result of the reconstruction is so good.

So I've had great support, surgery only, and the result looks fabulous, but it hasn't always been easy. My husband lost his first wife to cancer and was really affected when I was diagnosed. He had an overwhelming sense of anger and frustration which built up inside him, so much so that it did cause problems in our relationship. Not to the point where it would affect our marriage, but we did need the help of a counsellor to resolve things.

Right from the start I found that I would often need to make other people feel comfortable about what was happening to me, and bizarrely I found this therapeutic. Now I help to counsel women who are going through the same problems. I have always found talking helps; it's also a way for me to come to terms with everything myself.

Jackie

I believe everything happens for a reason

The surgeon sat and patiently explained everything to me. The recommended choice of action for my particular problem was a mastectomy.

I would expect that he is more used to people becoming lost for words or breaking down and crying, so he was a little taken aback when my immediate response was, 'can I have a reconstruction?' I presume he thought I was just a little shocked or disorientated as he asked me calmly if I wanted my partner, Geoff, to come in now.

Again I think my answer surprised him: 'no not yet'. I needed time to get everything sorted out in my head before speaking to Geoff. I was hugely concerned for him and how he would feel. Fifteen years ago he had come very close to losing his sister to this same awful disease. She had also undergone a mastectomy but needed chemotherapy and radiotherapy as well, the full works. Her survival chances were not rated as good, 40% they told her, but she is a fighter and I'm very pleased to say she is still with us today.

That's why I knew Geoff would be terrified for me, and I was right. He was far more affected by this whole episode than I was. He offered to completely change our lifestyle, to liberate ourselves from the chains of property ownership, travel the world and ease our foot off the gas pedal. I was overwhelmed that he was prepared to sacrifice so much but I didn't want to go through any drastic changes. Some readjustment yes, but overall I was happy with my lot.

So we have fine-tuned our lives. We have started to travel, and I have found this immensely enjoyable, but not travelling as an end in itself. I now also find it impossible to do anything that I don't want to do. Before all of this happened, I seemed to be fixing things for everyone around me but these days my focus has changed. I am still sympathetic and empathetic with others but a bigger slice of myself is reserved for me.

I have always been a calm and spiritual person and have trained as a Reiki Master. This is a form of natural energy healing where the underlying life force, *Chi*, is applied to strengthen someone's aura. I am convinced that this has smoothed my passage through breast cancer and accelerated my recovery.

I believe that everything happens for a reason. Breast cancer has happened to me to help Geoff and to encourage me to pass on my experiences in a positive way to others who have to follow this path which is not of their choosing.

Judith

I decided that the best way for me to cope was to look ahead and treat it as a huge learning curve

I am a very positive and down to earth person so in May 2003, when the breast care nurse told me the results, I don't remember going through any strong emotions. I was shocked of course. I was breast aware and checked myself regularly but had found nothing of concern during my own examinations.

I wanted life to carry on as normal, so even though I had been scheduled for a mastectomy in the first week of August I took the decision that we would still go on holiday at the end of July as planned. Whilst on holiday I took the time to read all of the information I had been given. It was then that I decided that the best way for me to cope with this new stage in my life was to look ahead, not dwell on it, and to treat it as a huge learning curve.

Following my mastectomy I realised that my body was incomplete. I was also not coping too well with the prosthesis, so I decided that I wanted to have reconstructive surgery. I opted to have a breast reduction on my right breast at the same time to give me a more balanced look.

Throughout my treatment I remained positive and active. I have a passion for collecting and restoring parasols and fans, and this occupied my mind when needed. After the mastectomy I took only four weeks off before returning to work and then an additional two weeks after reconstruction.

By 2004 I had a new bust and it was worth all of the worry and discomfort. I did everything I was told to do; I rested, exercised and applied oils and creams. Then in early 2006 I had a nipple formed, followed soon after by an areolar tattoo. I am very pleased with the result: I have had the equivalent of a complete body makeover!

I wouldn't say that breast cancer has changed my life. I take whatever life throws at me and deal with things as they come. That's my way of coping.

Susan

Does my bum look big in this?

Three years ago I was 48, happily married and settled into a comfortable family orientated routine. I was working as a relationship counsellor and my life was full, busy and fun. I was healthy but over the years I've had several cysts in my breasts drained. None of these had ever been anymore than a passing inconvenience so when I discovered another one I thought no more of it.

I made an appointment to have it drained and turned up at the hospital expecting the same routine. This time however it was different. The lump wasn't a cyst but a tumour and worse still, it was malignant.

As with many women given the same diagnosis I was numb with shock. My thoughts were on myself naturally, but also I was concerned how my family would cope if the worst happened, and also how they would deal with the changes that my illness would bring to all of us.

I wanted them to be shielded from it; but that proved impossible. At the time of my treatment our daughter was working for my husband, a dentist, as a receptionist. It was her job to cancel his appointments when he accompanied me on hospital visits. Most of his patients were unaware that she was our daughter and this proved difficult for her.

I was offered a procedure called an IGAP which involved taking fatty tissue, called a 'flap', from the lower part of one buttock and using this to create the breast. The operation had never been done in the UK before so I suppose I was a bit of a guinea pig! The operation was successful but when compared to my C cup natural breast, the reconstruction was a little small. Consequently I needed to have the whole thing redone four months later, taking a second 'flap' from my other buttock.

I remain positive and determined to live life to the full. I am where I am today because I had a strong and supportive family and a deep Christian faith, both of which sustained me during the darker moments.

I am very proud and confident with my new breasts. My husband is probably one of the few men who can get away with replying 'yes enormous' when I ask him 'does my bum looks big in this?' But only if I am asking him about my T shirt!

Liz

Reconstruction was positive; I felt I was taking control again

A topless model? Me? I've always been noted for my lack of curves … so what am I doing prancing about before the lens? Life changes when you've had breast cancer.

My cancer was discovered after my first routine screening, shortly after my 50th birthday. My reaction? Well, much the same as most, I expect: turmoil. I was bewildered. I wasn't ill, not even vaguely unwell. I had no lump, no physical clues. My cancer was found, so my surgeon tells me, through a lucky strike by the doctor who read the mammograms and performed the biopsy.

I was angry. My life, my plans, were being upset and taken out of my control. It was ages before I could bring myself to be grateful to the screening system and to the people who treated me.

I wasn't frightened, I never thought I'd die. Pigheaded, obviously, and I did get away lightly. Yes, I had invasive cancer, but it was self-contained; the lymph nodes were clear.

I was rocked back by the prospect of mastectomy. I think I always knew it was the likely option because I am small breasted, but I had hoped for the offending area to be winkled out. No go.

My husband was a rock; always there, always prepared to listen, listen, listen. He's the best.

I knew instinctively I wanted a reconstruction and I wanted it done immediately. This proved to be the best part of the business. It was positive and I felt that I was taking control again, choosing what I wanted done – instead of being done to. My surgeon did think I was bossy!

I was home within a week of the operation, walking half-a-mile to the local supermarket within days and working after two weeks. I was driving in a month and playing golf after two.

I am so glad I did it. I've got a breast made of living tissue, with a nipple made by taking half of the remaining one (no you can't see the join!) and I feel normal. My hope, in overcoming cancer, was not to change my life, not to climb Everest or buy a Lotus, but just to get back to normal and I've done it.

Lyndsey

A daughter, a spade and a dog. Each symbolises a part of my new life

Christmas 2005 was an uneasy time for me. After finding a lump in my breast earlier in December I was referred for a mammogram and scan. During the scan the consultant radiologist told me that he believed the tumour was malignant, but would need to take a biopsy to be sure. It was two days before Christmas so I had to wait until the New Year before I got the results.

With the exception of my husband Graham, I told nobody, not even my two daughters. I wanted Christmas to be as normal as possible.

The biopsy results confirmed the consultant's suspicions. But the whole experience seemed surreal. I knew I had breast cancer but I didn't feel any different.

My perspective of life has changed since my treatment. I have reduced my working hours so that I can have more time for myself. My home has become my sanctuary. It is so peaceful and regenerating. I can potter around in the garden and shut out the mad world around me.

I came to be photographed with my youngest daughter Gail, a spade and my dog. Each of these symbolised a part of my 'new life'. The spade represents my garden; my Labrador, the therapeutic and calming walks I undertake daily with him and my other five dogs; and Gail represents my family, because she and her sister Sharon, and of course Graham, adapted themselves and supported me when I most needed it. We are now all incredibly close.

I was rather nervous and needed a couple of glasses of bubbly to help me to relax before the photo session. But afterwards I was the one who was bubbling over. I found the experience very liberating. I didn't realise that I would feel so comfortable to be in the nude with someone I had never met before taking pictures of me for a book. I still have a body I can be proud of and a lovely cleavage to show that I am still a sexy lady!

Pat

I couldn't begin to comprehend what it would be like living with only one breast

Reconstruction has not changed me in any way, why should it? It was just another event in my life. I don't see my breast as being any different now to what it was before; it's still a part of my body.

I think I can also say the same of the illness itself: it hasn't made me change my life and I carry on as normal. I suppose you could say that I'm a strong woman. This has resulted from having to face hardship from early on in life. My first husband suffered a serious stroke and heart attack when I was just 32 years old and the upshot was that he could no longer work. So I became the 'bread-winner', a role which I maintained for over 20 years until he passed away. This was a great lesson in developing inner strength.

I could not even begin to comprehend what it would possibly be like living with only one breast. My immediate reaction when I was told that I would lose one was to tell my oncologist that he would simply have to give me another. I never realised at the time that this was actually possible!

Within two weeks I walked out of the office of my plastic surgeon under no illusions of what my body was about to go through. However this did nothing to deter me from this path. While I was waiting for the operation many friends and relatives who were afraid for me tried to convince me that I would be better off not going ahead with it. My husband assured me that it would make absolutely no difference to him, he would understand and respect my choice whatever it might be. But I had made my decision, so I can honestly say that I went ahead with the reconstruction for me and me alone.

I shall always be grateful to the surgeon and her team for restoring my life back to how it was. I feel well, and my life continues to be very full and active. Although I am now 68 years of age, sexually I feel as much a woman as I did before the operation. It certainly has made no difference to the feelings my husband has for me, and why should it? I am, and always will be, Pearl. I have not changed.

Pearl

After the operation I went through eighteen months of hell

Probably the worst thing for me psychologically was that the mastectomy robbed me of my femininity. I felt mutilated. I started wearing high necked, baggy clothes and, even though I wore a prosthesis, began hunching my shoulders so that other people would not notice my shape.

After the operation I went through eighteen months of hell, counting down the days until I could have reconstruction. During that time I hid my body from everyone, including Bob, my husband. Yes, he was very supportive and took every opportunity to reassure me but my confidence had hit rock bottom and I wasn't open to reason.

Before my breast cancer I lived twenty-four–seven for my children and grandchildren. My family were my life. But during my illness the roles were reversed; they really took care of me and helped me break out of my crisis of confidence. I remember once losing my prosthesis in front of them. I was mortified but they took it all in their stride: 'look it moved, it's alive!' one said. Everyone was soon in fits of laughter, me included.

I was resolute about having reconstruction but I was seriously overweight and the plastic surgeon instructed me to lose some before she would operate. My willpower kicked in and I surprised her by losing forty-two pounds (that's nineteen kilos for the younger generation), in only three months!

Today, with a new breast and fifty-six pounds lighter, my life is far more balanced. I have become more outgoing and do more things for myself. I have joined an internet-based support group for breast cancer survivors and even flew to meet with some of them in Scotland. I would never even go on a plane before this!

My confidence and determination are greater than they have ever been. I have invested in a brand new wardrobe, changed my style, wear younger, trendier clothes and even have a bikini for the summer. My reconstruction has changed my life and I can sum up how I feel in just one word. 'Fantastic!'

Shirley

I wasn't expecting miracles; you can't make a silk purse out of a sow's ear

It has been three months now since the finishing touches were put on to my reconstructed breasts and I'm getting back to leading the normal life of a 70 year old. Yes that's right, a 70 year old. One who goes swimming with her grandchildren, can play tennis with them without having to clutch her cleavage before bending down, and can wear low necks, 'V' necks, round necks, any flipping necks she fancies. Now I'm not sure that the image of me rushing around playing tennis with my grandchildren is necessarily a good one, but who cares. I have wobbly bits again and I did miss them after 50 odd years.

This wasn't my first brush with breast cancer. I had a lumpectomy and radiotherapy back in 1990, after which I had thirteen cancer-free years until I noticed some small, white calcium deposits on my nipple. I was advised that a bilateral mastectomy would allow me to live out my natural lifespan. So I had a choice, to be alive with no breasts or dead with two. Not much of a choice really was it?

Some may say I am a little too old to be bothered with breast reconstruction, in fact some did. My breast care nurse told me to wait, and in any case, she added, most old people decide not to bother in the end. But not me, I'm not old; I'm only 40 in my head! Fortunately my plastic surgeon agreed with me, but I do think she had to convince a few others of the fact.

When I awoke after the operation I really looked an oddity. I had had a double mastectomy and was expecting a double reconstruction too. But because one of my breasts had undergone radiotherapy there was some problem with the skin, so I was only half finished. I had a beautiful new breast on my left side, and another one on my stomach waiting to be moved up. It was a little difficult to buy clothes then I must say!

Now, as you can see, I am completed. The second procedure was much easier and I managed afterwards without morphine or painkillers, only Classic FM to soothe me.

Even at my age femininity is very important and your breasts are a huge part of this. I wasn't expecting miracles; you can't make a silk purse out of a sow's ear anyway. Actually now I'm not so sure, they seem to have managed, twice in my case.

Stella

I just stood in my surgeon's office and refused to leave until she agreed to do it

In October 2004 I decided to go on a diet and to exercise. By March 2005 I had lost almost two stone, my body shape had changed and my breasts had become smaller. Then one day my husband remarked that as well as reducing in size, my right breast seemed to have developed a lump and nagged me to go and get it checked out.

I was very relieved to be told by the consultant that my lump was a cyst, which he removed straight away. Great! Then, since I was there, he offered me a mammogram, just to be on the safe side. This showed that the right breast, where the initial lump was found was fine, but the left breast showed some dark cells. Further tests showed these to be cancerous pre-tumours and, what's more, there were too many for any course of action except breast removal.

Steve, my husband, helped me to research reconstruction options on the internet so when I went for my second appointment with the plastic surgeon I was sure of the reconstruction I wanted. But she told me that the IGAP operation was too complicated and she had decided to stop doing it. By now I think I had developed a rather stubborn streak and was certainly becoming more assertive, so I refused to accept that this was no longer available. I just stood in her office and refused to leave until she agreed to do it! I guess I must have been persuasive, or I simply wore her down, because she finally relented. My reconstruction was very successful and this gave the surgeon the confidence to carry on with this procedure, which will benefit so many more women.

I was working full-time when I was diagnosed and really enjoying my work but I soon needed time off for my treatment. This period of reflection, exclusively for me, seemed like a breath of fresh air and I benefited from it greatly. So much so that I felt trapped when I returned to work. I tried to go part-time but the feeling remained, so reluctantly I gave up work completely.

Going through an experience like this is life changing and I have realised that time is too precious and too short not to enjoy it. I now love my new, relaxed lifestyle and I am much happier in myself. Simple pleasures seem so much richer now. I power-walk with my neighbour, tend my allotment and enjoy more family time with my husband and two girls. I don't think I could ever go back to the lifestyle I had before.

Sue

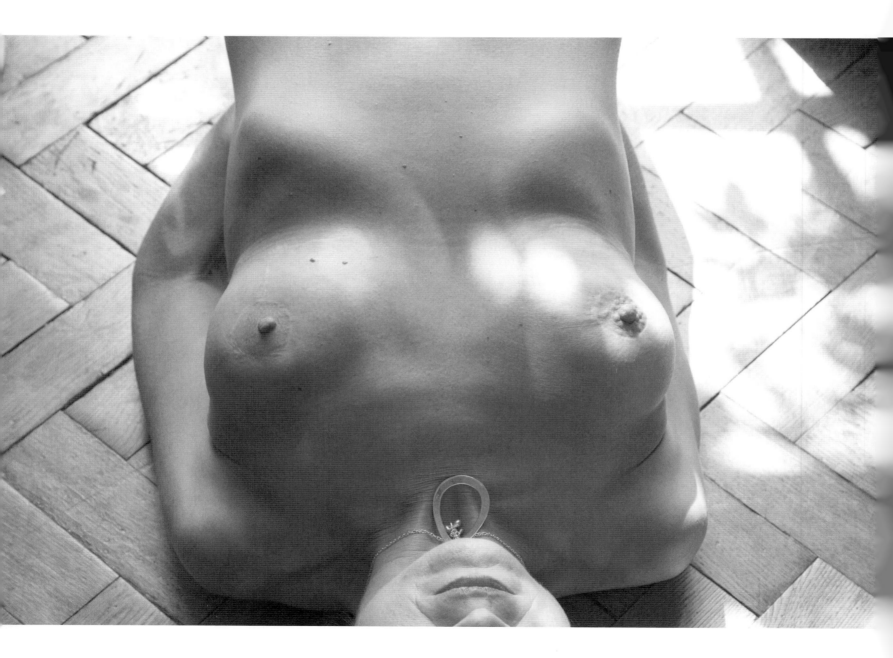

My new breasts are bigger and fill the leathers nicely

My passion for bikes stems from the freedom they allow me: panoramic vision, flexibility, confidence, no need to wait for the rest of the world. Now with my new breasts I've regained that confidence I'd lost. They are bigger than before, so now they fill the leathers nicely. Initially they were very small, A cup. Alan, my partner would refer to them as fried eggs.

But my initial decision to have reconstruction was as much for practical as cosmetic reasons. I never wore a bra before my mastectomy but now I had no choice. I needed one to hold my prosthesis in place. I opted for an implant and after the expander had been left in for a few months to stretch the skin, my new breast was going to be bigger than my right. So I decided to have a balancing implant to even them up.

It all began in September 1999 when I got a recall from a routine mammogram. I froze; I knew it was going to be bad news. I had to go for an immediate needle biopsy, but they weren't able to complete it under local anaesthetic so it had to be re-done under general. Before the operation I spent the worst night of my life distressed and alone in a four-bed ward. Ten days later I was told that I needed a mastectomy without delay. I was told to go home and pack a bag, my mastectomy was scheduled for the next day. I was offered a reconstruction at the same time, but with less than ten minutes to decide, shocked and disorientated, I decided against it.

I am a fighter and was determined not to let this affect my life. After the 'big op' was over, my head cleared and I was ready to move on with a much more positive attitude.

Life doesn't always run as smoothly as planned. In 2001, while I was still undergoing reconstruction, a hit-and-run driver broke my leg in three places.

In many respects I found the broken leg even more difficult to cope with because it left me incapacitated for far longer. Even the simplest tasks seemed impossible. I had to fit my reconstruction around my leg operations which certainly prolonged the treatment. In all, I underwent eight breast and five leg operations, including two bone grafts, over six years.

Alan has been my soul-mate for many years and supported me throughout; having someone so close has made a huge difference to me. It would have been much harder without him.

Chic

I am taking part in this photo shoot, liberated and proud

It really is true that you don't appreciate some things until they are gone, and it isn't always the biggest and most obvious losses which affect you the most.

I had always taken my breasts for granted, right up until the day I was told that one of them was to be taken away. I was terrified at the thought and particularly conscious about losing my nipple. I was 31, single, and my breasts represented my femininity and my ability to be a mother and feed a baby. I knew I could have reconstruction, but without my nipple I was worried that I would always look and feel lopsided.

Chemotherapy also brought its changes and I became concerned when I began losing my hair. My brother brought me down to earth. 'Just so long as you don't look like Gollum' (from Lord of the Rings) was his rather black-humoured response.

A little later I decided to have my eyebrows temporarily tattooed because my face looked barren without them. I was told that they would look very dark for at least the following week. Not a problem, unless you are called Ming the Merciless! Incidentally why was it that I still needed to shave my legs when everywhere else hair was dropping out of its own accord? Laughter is great therapy and helps to bring things back into proportion. Life may be short, that is not of our choosing, but it need not be spent in a cloud of depression. That is within our control.

Not having reconstructive surgery was never an option for me, because of my age and being single. I felt I wanted to give myself every opportunity to carry on with life as normally as possible. It has helped me to cope with the emotional rollercoaster that you travel on with cancer. I have had my second breast removed and reconstructed and I am now embarking on round three of chemo, but without the additional worry of my physical appearance, which is very important. Of course it can't cure my illness, but taking care of how I look and feel is half the battle.

As for my nipple, I now have a graft and tattoo (my tittoo!) which is amazing and not at all lopsided; in fact I almost feel that my surgery is a work of art. I have felt bizarrely compelled to show people my new nipple and have been frustrated to realise that it's not always appropriate! My confidence has grown too, so here I am taking part in a Page 3 equivalent photo shoot, liberated and proud; a place I never thought I would be three years ago.

Emma

My confidence comes from a different, stronger, person

I have always been an independent woman with a love of languages, so in 1983 it was no surprise that I uprooted and moved to Luxembourg. I settled into a wonderful cosmopolitan lifestyle, got married, and raised three wonderful sons. Life was a breeze ... until June 2002.

I noticed numbness in my breast; there was no lump but a biopsy confirmed cancer. I underwent a mastectomy and lymph node removal, chemotherapy and radiotherapy, and was told that the prognosis was good.

The harshness of the chemotherapy was offset by the lovely sense of peace I found during my daily walks in the forest near our house. One morning I discovered a hide, presumably for bird-watchers, set high in a large tree. I felt compelled to climb up the ladder and sat in awe of the beauty of the forest below me. The dappled sunlight filtered through leaves that were vibrant and full of life, and which seemed to echo the process going on in my body, renewing and recharging me.

Telling the boys (then 13, 15 and 6) was incredibly difficult. I was honest with them, and tried to laugh about things, but inside I felt quite vulnerable. Having previously been quite relaxed about nudity at home, I kept myself hidden from them, not wanting to shock or frighten them. However, one day, my eldest son came to chat to me as I was about to get into the bath. Feeling self-conscious, I began to stall for time. He waited, patiently at first and then said 'please just get in the bath, you're still my mum'. My youngest son had his own ideas, and on glimpsing the merest hint of my scar, simply asked me if I had become a zombie... I am so proud of how my three sons coped and supported me.

Three years on and fed up with wearing a prosthesis, it was time for action. Unfortunately I was not offered the type of reconstructive surgery that I had once read about, using my own flesh and blood to recreate a breast. However, my mother-in-law kindly sent me an article about such an operation being performed in Norwich. I shall always be indebted to her for this.

There is no question that the quality of my life has improved immeasurably since the reconstruction. I naturally feel more confident in my appearance, but that confidence now comes from within – from a different, stronger person. Doctors may admire the results from a 'technical' point of view, but by far the best compliment paid to me was when a mammography nurse commented on my post-holiday suntan before noticing, in amazement, my new breast.

Debbie

Reconstruction? No. I was told to count myself lucky to be alive

When I was 26 my mother died after eighteen months of sickness and pain following a radical mastectomy, which she described as making her feel like a freak. Ever since then I carried the anxiety that I would also develop breast cancer.

Ten years later I married. We were really happy and began concentrating on building our home. Then a year later, in 1979, I felt discomfort in my right breast, like an insect bite. I was devastated to discover a small but significant lump just above my right nipple. I knew immediately it was cancer.

I had read in an American magazine that it was possible to have an implant, so as soon as a mastectomy was mentioned I requested a reconstruction. I was however told to count myself lucky to be alive.

When I woke up from the operation, in place of my breast was a line of ugly black stitches which I couldn't bear to look at. I was distraught and thought that Anthony, my husband, would no longer find me attractive. Happily my fear was totally unfounded, I could not have wished for a more understanding and caring man. All the same I started to get depressed and suffered from agoraphobia, which was made worse by the medication I was given to induce an early menopause.

The first time I went to the local swimming pool I was sitting on the side enjoying the sunshine as usual when I suddenly realised things were not the same: a piece of me was missing. I was gripped by a panic attack and barely made it home. On another occasion I forgot to take my prosthesis, so I filled the cup of my swimsuit with a couple of socks. I was mortified when someone fished my socks out of the water!

In time I gained confidence but whenever I saw myself in a mirror I was reminded. I was never able to move on.

Over the years I asked every new GP about a reconstruction. The response was always the same: 'Learn to live with it'. Then a couple of years ago a lady doctor finally referred me to a plastic surgeon. Last December I underwent a reconstruction, twenty-seven years after my mastectomy.

Conventionally most women opt for a nipple tattoo, but I didn't want that so I had a special tattoo. My husband and I chose it together. It was not done without some pain but we think it is lovely and well worth it. I am so happy and excited to have a new breast after all this time that I spend hours in lingerie departments. I now own twenty-nine new bras ...

Mary

My GP was the first person to tell me that I could actually live

How could I have cancer? I didn't know anyone who had had it and lived. I was only 40, far too young to die. My head was spinning; I could only think of my two boys. I went home to speak to my mother; she was devastated as my father had died only a few months earlier. I didn't sleep for days, I was drowning.

The next week I went to see my GP and was amazed to discover that she herself had had breast cancer. She had even gone on to have more children after her treatment. I have no doubt that this was my turning point. She was the first person to tell me that people can get better, and that I could actually live. My assumption that I would surely die was wrong.

After the mastectomy I could really start living. The thing was out; what a relief. I tolerated the 6 months of chemotherapy and 10 weeks of radiotherapy. I lost my hair of course, but I didn't wear a wig; just a bandana and a shocking pink cap.

I carried on as normal with my work and looking after my family. That is what we do, isn't it? Anyway I had no choice, my children were young: Andrew 3 and Christopher 7, they needed me. It was important not to frighten them, so we didn't tell them about the cancer, just that I needed treatment and would lose my hair for a while. I was busy and kept a brave face.

My husband Terry supported me and came with me to all the appointments and my friends and family helped me tremendously. After the chemotherapy, we got a dog to help me relax and make me exercise. He helps to calm me down, forces me to go slow and not charge around all the time.

The one thing I never came to terms with was the big ugly scar; I hated it. Later on my hatred transferred to the prosthesis which was uncomfortable and unsightly. I refused to let Terry see me naked. I stopped wearing T-shirts and hid behind high necked tops. I even gave up swimming because I couldn't bring myself to use the changing rooms and detested those mastectomy swim suits.

Reconstruction has helped me considerably. Goodbye mastectomy swim suit, hello bikini. I swim 2 to 3 times a week again and my scar is a fading memory. I have rediscovered what I have to live for, and am back making the most of my life.

Gill

I'm no longer searching for that elusive, missing 'something'...

In 2004 at 32, I was fit and sporty. Winters were for skiing, summers for rock climbing. I was career minded and future focused, but life was not complete. So it was that over dinner in Paris on St Valentine's day I told my husband Neil that I wanted to try for a baby.

I came off the pill and had a full check up including a breast examination; all was well. By the summer of that year I had something growing inside me, but a breast tumour was not what we were expecting.

It was a huge shock. Breast cancer doesn't happen to women of my age. There was so much I still wanted to accomplish; I didn't want to die.

Hope returned after meeting my oncologist. He dismissed many things we had been previously told and started to calm the fears that were enveloping us. Nevertheless, he said I needed chemotherapy and radiotherapy immediately.

I never thought about the possibility that I might lose my breast. I was convinced the chemo would work; the tumour would shrink down then they would pop it out. A short blast of radiotherapy and I would be left with a small scar and a tan; olive skinned French girls don't burn like their paler-skinned neighbours.

But my tumour proved resistant to chemical attack, even when the drug was changed to a French one! It needed to be removed and with it my breast.

Afterwards I never had a complex about my body, but it was important for me to regain the symmetry that two breasts gave me. I have always loved lingerie and how sensual it makes me feel. Nothing is sensual about a prosthesis. Moreover, it became a constant reminder of what I'd been through.

It surprises a lot of people that I view the whole breast cancer experience as something positive that has happened to me. My life has been enriched by the people I have met along the way. Yes, it has changed my life; I have learned to live in the present and realised how important it is to enjoy simple things. I'm no longer searching for that elusive, missing 'something'. I didn't know what it was, but it prevented me from appreciating what I had. I am very happy with my life today.

For me the circle is complete and I am thrilled to be four months pregnant, which I still cannot believe after all I have been through. With love and support from the people around you everything becomes possible. Never give up, keep on fighting and you will win.

Chrystèle

I needed reconstruction but wanted something better than a chicken fillet

'Right second time', that seems to be the thread that runs through my story.

In May of 2003, when I was 29 years old, I underwent a lumpectomy to remove a small pea-sized lump from my left breast. When they removed the dressings the result didn't seem at all bad and I left the hospital relieved and pleased. However a week later I was told that they had found another cancer in the tissue area they had removed during the operation. This time the diagnosis was far more serious and I would need a mastectomy.

I remember that the day of the operation was very hard for me, especially with the thought of what I would be losing. Months of chemotherapy followed which was made all the harder for only having one breast. Life was proving very difficult and I found myself hiding my body from both my husband and my children.

I knew that psychologically I needed a reconstruction, but I wanted something better than a chicken fillet. After discussing the options with my plastic surgeon I decided on an implant. I have to say that this was against the advice of my surgeon, who felt that this was not the best option for me, but I was insistent. I went through the whole process of skin stretching and implanting and at first the end result appeared fine, but as time went on I became less and less happy with it. So during one of my checkups with the surgeon I asked her opinion. 'Awful' she replied honestly. This was a relief for me, not knowing what a good reconstruction did or didn't look like; I had nothing to compare them against.

Now I put my faith completely in the surgeon and told her to do whatever she could to improve them. The implant was removed and she has given me a far more natural and realistic breast using tissue taken from my tummy.

It has now been five years since my first operation and I feel that my new breast looks as good as my old one. Nobody seems to be able to tell the difference when I tell them what I've been through.

So now you see, cancer surgery twice, breast reconstruction twice, but now I'm twice as happy with the result than I ever imagined I would be.

Suzy

DIARY OF A PROJECT

December 2004. Wednesday: breast reconstruction clinic. These clinics are always overbooked and exhausting, but the women are wonderful and we often dissolve into laughter. I know that once they rediscover their sense of humour they will be all right. For a while now I have been thinking that I would like to find a way of representing this spirit in a book. After clinic I have an appointment with the Mentor rep., Elin Turner. She has been trying in vain to see me to convince me to use Mentor implants for about a year. She offers me the book: *Reconstructing Aphrodite*, by Terry Lorant, perhaps as a sweetener. (I understood from her years later that it was a standard joke at the Mentor office: who would finally succeed in speaking to Miss Sassoon!)

The book is FABULOUS and represents so much of what I want to project!

I am inspired, I want to use a similar format, but the book will be more European and, of course, written by a plastic surgeon rather than a photographer and showing my patients' incredible inner strength and courage.

I start asking patients if they would like to be in my book, being photographed topless outdoors somewhere. Most say yes, no doubt thinking it will never happen. I put their names on stickers at the back of my diary.

October 2005. I mention to Elin that I am interested in writing the book. She reports back a couple of days later that Mentor Medical Systems will help.

January 2006. I phone James Ruddy, deputy editor of my local paper, who arranges a pub meeting with Cris de Boos. He agrees in principle to publish the book. All seems very easy. Just need to find location and photographer. My plan is to publish in October. I want a female photographer, preferably someone well known, who has a connection with breast cancer. Why not Koo Stark? I get the number of her agent, but whenever I phone there is always an answering machine; I don't leave a message.

May 2006. So busy with targets and committees I have done nothing about the book. I have been mentioning the project to patients though and lots are willing to be photographed (virtually all!).

September 2006. Well, the book certainly isn't going to be out this October! Bronwen, one of my patients, leaves a message: two friends are putting a farm and a beautiful garden in North Norfolk at our disposal for the photo-shoot. I still need a photographer. I mention the book to Chrystèle (another patient) and ask her if she knows anyone, preferably female. She embraces the project and starts looking for photographers. Soon she is doing telephone interviews.

November 2006. Chrystèle has selected a photographer. I meet him; he shows some beautiful

pictures in his portfolio, he is keen. Of course he has no experience of photographing women who have had breast cancer, but then who has? I think I am happy, in fact I worry about how comfortable some of my patients will be in front of a man.

A week later I operate on Andrea! As we chat in the days postoperatively, I mention my project. Kevin her husband informs me that she is a photographer, in fact a very good one. I smile politely. I already have a photographer now, but ...

January 2007. Chrystèle has spoken to Andrea, seen some of her work and says she is the one for the project. I decide on the photo-shoot in May, when it will be warm.

15 April 2007. The weather has been fantastic all month. I go and visit the locations that Bronwen's friends have put at our disposal. They are just right. I love the concept of harsh machinery contrasting with soft human bodies. And they have a pond, and animals, in fact lots of possible backdrops. Bronwen then says: 'Of course you will need someone to do the makeup'. What makeup? How on earth would I know anyone who does makeup? I am a surgeon, for heaven's sake.

May 2007. The weather has been awful and more rain is forecast. One week before the shoot, once I know that Andrea has actually booked her flight from Ireland and will stay 3 days, I phone the patients. I have nearly 90 stickers in the back of my diary of patients whom I have previously asked if they would pose. I have three hours to find about 20 of them. It proves remarkably easy. Most are at home and when contacted, they all reply: 'Why not?' Hurrah!! I start sending directions.

12 May 2007. One week to go. I need a laptop for the project. I am overworked and exhausted. I catch sight of myself in a mirror at the department store, I look frightful: haggard and drawn. Concealer urgently needed. Like a zombie I turn right towards the beauty department. 'Hello Miss Sassoon', a clear voice rings out from behind the counter as I point to the item I need. I stare dumbly at Hannah, one of my ex (non reconstructive) patients ... and dare. 'Do you do makeup?' 'Would you come to North Norfolk and make up 23 ladies over 3 days?' 'When?' 'Next week', I answer. Like everything in this project, it seems easy. She has never done a photo-shoot, but she wants to do it.

Debbie phones: she is bringing two cases of champagne from Luxembourg. She, Liz and her husband Nick, Andrea, Chrystèle and Neil are staying in North Norfolk with me. Will the plumbing cope?

19 May 2007. Debbie arrived yesterday. I take her to Holt to stock up on more champagne and food for the shoot. I show her the Stables antiques shop in Bayfield Hall. What a wonderful setting that would be for the shoot! Because Debbie is there, I

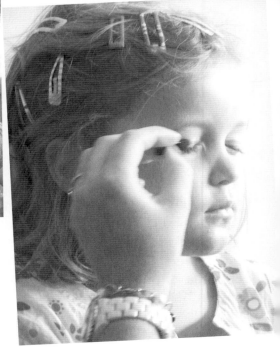

find the courage to ask the person in the shop if we could possibly shoot here. Forty-five minutes later Caroline Combe, the owner, phones and says yes. We go to meet her on Monday evening, and she gives us free rein of the Hall and the grounds, and sets up a whole preparation room for us for the last day of the shoot on Tuesday.

Everywhere we seem to encounter kindness and goodwill. Life without bureaucracy! I wish working in the NHS was so straightforward. The only problem is the weather, forecast to be bad; we will just have to have lots of shots with umbrellas.

20 May 2007. It is 10.45 am. Morning coffee at the cottage, excitement all round as we are getting ready to leave for Bradfield Hall Farm. Andrea will have arrived at Stansted Airport by now and Barry from Strong Cars will pick her up and take her straight to the farm. It is all so easy. Nothing can go wrong now, so I start to declare it to all. At that precise moment Barry's wife Jenny knocks on the door, (no mobile phone signal in the village) having run to tell me: Andrea is not on the flight! She has not landed at Stansted. I feel dizzy. This will be the end of the project. Can I face cancelling all these patients? Nobody has Andrea's mobile phone number. At Barry's house we use the landline to phone Andrea's husband, Kevin. He calls her: she is at Stansted somewhere. Eventually Barry and Andrea find each other. All's well.

The weather had been awful all week but cleared that morning. It remained fabulous for the whole time of the shoot. We shot at Bradfield Hall Farm, in Sandra Bullock's beautiful garden at Swafield, at Bayfield Hall and on Sunday night, on Weybourne beach. I still had not seen Andrea's work, yet trusted Chrystèle's judgement, but was very nervous on the Sunday as I knew exactly what I wanted to see projected in the photographs in my usual obsessional way. I wanted Mario Testino. I needn't have worried. I got what I wanted. Within half an hour I relaxed, left everyone to get on with things and played with my cat.

We still do not have a title for the book. I want something with Boudica in it: The Spirit of Boudica perhaps, to represent the local element, the women's courage, beauty etc? Everyone contributes ideas over endless champagne: 'Carry on Constructing, Tits R Us, It's all gone Tits up, Does my Bum look big in this, Boobs I've made, Boudica's Bust, You should have kept your Vest on, How to keep aBreast of the Situation, Privates on Parade, Titillation, Nipples galore, Bosom buddies, Boudica's Bosoms', and so on. Someone says : THE BOUDICA WITHIN. We're sorted! Later on Chrystèle will add the subtitle.

29 May 2007. I am back at work and receive a letter of thanks from Mary, a recent patient,

together with photographs. Instead of having a nipple reconstructed, she has gone and had almost her whole breast tattooed with flowers and a nymph. Absolutely fabulous. She has to be in the book! I write her story with her, borrow Neil's camera and take 45 'artistic shots' of her myself. I get them couriered to Ireland. The verdict on every single one: unusable. Neil has to retake the pictures.

10 June 2007. Andrea flies to Stansted and we meet with Chrystèle and Neil to select the photographs. I have been told about the need for copyright for everything; I worry.

23 June 2007. Penny Morgan has asked a publisher friend about copyright. Apparently he wants to publish the book. He comes up to Norwich. I don't know what to do. He runs a big publishing house in London, has access to designers, presses abroad ...

I phone my friend Robert, as usual my saviour. His friend Pedro has designed for books, and will help. I will stay with my local publisher.

2 July 2007. Most of the book is with the publisher.

BREAST RECONSTRUCTION INFORMATION

(For definitions of medical terms, please see the glossary on p. 124)

Reconstructive breast surgery is one of the most common procedures that the plastic surgeon is called upon to perform. With increasing numbers of breast cancer cases annually, and with surgery still the mainstay of therapy, the number of women seeking reconstruction is at an all time high.

The first major decision you need to make is whether or not to actually have a reconstruction. *The Boudica Within* features women who opted to have one, and feel very positive about the impact it has had on their lives. I certainly believe that it should be available to you. On the other hand you should never feel compelled to have reconstruction. It means more surgery, and of course there is potential for complications; in addition rebuilding a breast is certainly more involved than a lumpectomy or mastectomy. It is really a process which often involves several operations over a period of months, although after the initial big procedure most others will be relatively minor and done under local anaesthetic. So for various reasons you may not wish to go ahead, or maybe not at this time. To my mind the most important thing is that it is your body and you must have a say.

If you decide to proceed the next decision is *when*. It has become increasingly popular to reconstruct the breast at the same time as the mastectomy, thereby preventing a period of complete absence of the breast. Not all women want this, as some prefer to deal with one thing at a time: first get rid of the cancer, and later think of having a new breast. This can be quite a difficult decision and may be too much to cope with when you are dealing with a diagnosis of cancer.

The emotional advantages of immediate reconstruction are clear, the scarring is reduced and the whole process is easier and faster; you wake up with a new breast and often with a new nipple. All you then need is the areola (the pink bit) tattooed and some shaping, often under local anaesthetic. From a surgeon's point of view, since most of the skin and breast shape is preserved, it is much easier to obtain a beautiful result in just one operation. However, not all women are candidates for immediate reconstruction, particularly if postoperative radiotherapy is needed. You should discuss with your oncology surgeon and your plastic surgeon whether this option is suitable for you.

In the case of delayed reconstruction (over half the cases in my unit), after the mastectomy is performed and the wounds are all healed, I prefer to wait three months for the tissues to mature and soften, that is if chemotherapy or radiation therapy is not required. If either is necessary, I would expect you to complete these therapies, and then wait at least 6 months before beginning the reconstruction surgery. That way your tissues have the opportunity to recover.

There are many techniques available to the reconstructive surgeon looking to improve a woman's appearance after a mastectomy. The final choice depends on her wishes, body shape, available tissue, skin quality, appearance of the opposite breast and health. The realistic goal will be the improvement of appearance and not the perfect replacement of the breast. I have noticed however that women often say at the first consultation that they just want something to fill their bra, yet as their self-esteem improves after the reconstruction they become more critical and demand perfection, which I tell myself is a good thing.

The key to a successful reconstruction is careful selection to match you with the operation which is most appropriate. The result is influenced by the reconstruction chosen, the quality of the tissues and the quality of the surgery. In order to prepare for the surgery and sail through it with the minimum chance of complications you should become as healthy as possible and if you smoke, quit.

A brief overview of the options follows. This is not an exhaustive list. All surgeons have personal preferences, and I discuss the options which I believe are the best or the most commonly performed in Britain at present.

If you have a partial mastectomy or wide local excision.

As this involves leaving a significant portion of the original breast intact most patients will have radiotherapy following this operation in order to destroy possible lingering tumour cells. The common options are:

1. Moving other parts of the breast around to fill the defect at the time of the excision. It uses basic principles of plastic surgery and has recently become popular and been given a name: therapeutic mammaplasty. This can produce superb results but you need to have a large enough breast of course to provide the tissue to relocate. The other breast can be reduced or lifted to match as well.

2. Filling the defect by bringing your own tisue from elsewhere to restore the shape with what is called a 'flap'. This is usually in the form of a 'local flap' where tissue is moved around without interrupting the blood supply, but sometimes a 'free flap' where tissue with its blood supply is detached and then reattached to the breast area with microsurgery. The most common local flaps come from the back either with muscle (latissimus dorsi flap) or without (TAP flap). All these flaps are named after their muscles or their

arteries, so they are often abbreviated. When using tissue from a free flap, I prefer a perforator flap which is just skin and fat without muscle.

3. The third option for filling the defect later on is lipomodelling/lipofilling. Here fat is taken from another part of the body by liposuction, concentrated and injected very carefully back into the breast. This is a fairly new procedure and quite promising. It can be done as a day case, under local or general anaesthetic.

If you have a mastectomy:

The whole breast must be reconstructed in this case.

IMPLANT RECONSTRUCTION

It is the simplest procedure of all and involves the placement of a silicone or saline implant beneath the muscle of the chest wall at the time of mastectomy. This can occasionally be inserted as a delayed reconstruction if the implant is small. Incisions are usually either through the mastectomy scar or wound, or placed at the inferior position of the newly created breast. This is a quick operation and no other scars are created on the body. There may be some limitations of arm motion for four to six weeks. The great majority of implants inserted are still silicone implants. The results can be very nice for smaller pert breasts with firm skin. On the other hand, if the other breast is large, droopy and has softened from breast feeding several children, the best you will get here is symmetry in a bra, unless you have something done to the other side.

In such cases the other breast can be firmed up with an implant as well, or lifted or reduced if you want to obtain a better match.

Please note that implants are man-made, feel firmer than normal breasts and do require replacing after a period of time.

TISSUE EXPANSION

Often the simple placement of an implant is not possible because the skin is too tight after a mastectomy. In this case new tissue must be created either by expansion of local tissue or transfer of a flap of healthy tissue from somewhere else.

Tissue expansion is accomplished under a general anaesthetic by the placement of a 'tissue expander' beneath the muscle of the chest wall. Expanders initially resemble a flat balloon. During visits to the outpatient clinic over the next six to twelve weeks, sterile saline water is injected into the expander to stretch the surrounding skin to the point where the pocket is big enough to accept the proper size implant. Effectively we are slowly stretching the skin in the same way as it does during pregnancy. There is some discomfort with each expansion but you can usually continue normal activity. Removal of the expander and placement of the final permanent implant is done during a second anaesthetic. Some types of expander don't need to be changed. They can stay in. They are usually a mixture of saline and silicone.

Patients with radiated skin or excessively thin skin are not usually candidates for tissue expansion as the tissues will not stretch.

FLAP RECONSTRUCTION

The condition of your chest wall may dictate the need for extra tissue: a flap. This is the case when the mastectomy is very tight or has been subjected to radiotherapy which stops the skin from stretching. So you need to bring in health tissue from elsewhere which will be able to stretch. The main options include moving tissue either from the back (as a local flap), or from the lower abdomen or buttocks (as a free flap) to replace the missing skin.

From the Back
The classic LATISSIMUS DORSI flap: skin, fat and the *latissimus dorsi* muscle are used, with an expander or implant underneath to provide more bulk to the breast mound. The muscle is a broad muscle in the back, which can be transferred, along with a portion of overlying skin and fat, to the chest. The 'new' tissue along with an implant or expander creates the new breast mound. Whilst beautiful results can be expected, this is a more complicated procedure than using a tissue expander alone, and requires about three hours of surgery and several days in hospital. It is moderately painful, and you may encounter weakness of your shoulder muscles so beware if you are a keen rock climber, golfer or tennis player.

The EXTENDED LATISSIMUS DORSI flap takes all the available fat and all of the muscle. It thus gives you a bigger breast mound and avoids the need to use an implant. This operation takes longer, and requires a lot of post-operative physiotherapy and shoulder exercises to build up strength again.

The stay in hospital is about a week for the extended *latissimus dorsi* flap, and there is some pain afterwards as muscle is divided.

From the Abdomen and Buttocks
The more sophisticated tissue transfer techniques do not use implants – they use only the patient's tissues (so are called autologous reconstructions) – the results can be far more natural and they last longer. The extended *latissimus dorsi* is an autologous reconstruction from the back. Other operations bring tissue from abdomen, buttocks or inner thighs.

SOME CLINICAL PICTURES

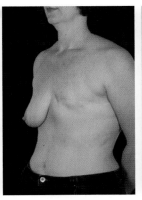

Delayed latissimus dorsi flap + implant
Before   After

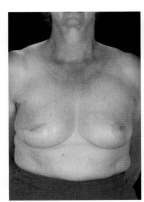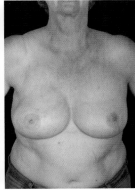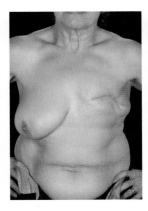

Immediate latissimus dorsi flap + implant
Before   After

Delayed SIEA flap
Before   After

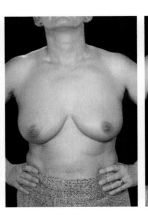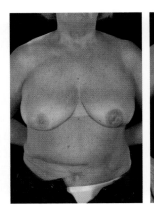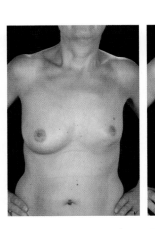

Immediate DIEP flap
Before   After

Immediate DIEP flap
Before   After

Immediate IGAP flap
Before   After

My preference is for **PERFORATOR FLAP** techniques, where a breast is fashioned out of a flap of skin and fat with its blood vessels, and muscle is not sacrificed. I believe that muscle is there for function, so if possible we should leave it in place.

Perforator flaps are classed as: DIEP, SIEA, PUP and others from the abdomen; SGAP and IGAP from the buttocks; and TAP from the back. They are all named after their artery, as described in the glossary on page 124.

Perforator flaps have gained in popularity in the last 10 years as more plastic surgeons have been trained to do them. To my mind they are the gold standard in reconstructive microsurgery of the breast.

These flaps take skin and fat with one single artery and vein from the abdomen or the buttocks which are then transferred and sewn to the chest. The operations are delicate and involve complex microsurgery (the use of small needles and stitch material to sew fine blood vessels together under an operating microscope). Once blood circulation through the tissue is restored it can heal in its new position.

The advantage to you is that no muscle is taken with the flap, only skin and fat. Therefore function is hardly compromised. The risk of weakness and hernia of the abdominal wall in the case of the DIEP and other perforator flaps of the abdomen is minimised, and a mesh to reinforce the abdomen is not needed. In the case of the IGAP flap you reduce the chance of pressure on nerves and pain when seated, compared to the same flap taken with muscle.

There is usually enough tissue to build a breast without the use of an implant, so the result should be permanent. The abdomen is tightened as in a 'tummy tuck' or the buttock is sewn as in a 'buttock lift'.

It is major intricate surgery and takes about 6 to 8 hours for the lone plastic surgeon, and, on average, 4 hours if two experienced surgeons are involved. (Of course many operations are teaching cases and take longer.) The stay in hospital is about 6 days, ie the same as the latissimus dorsi flap. It is a less painful operation than the latissimus dorsi flap as muscle is not divided. There is a failure rate, which varies from less than 1% to 10% in different units. The more experienced the surgeon, the better and the faster he/she gets at these difficult operations. With the DIEP and SIEA flaps, the tissue is taken from the abdomen, and you end up with a tummy tuck. The scar is quite long, and is often a bit higher than that of the standard cosmetic tummy tuck. For the SGAP or IGAP flap the tissue comes from the buttock, either the upper or the lower buttock. The scar is on the upper buttock with the SGAP and on the buttock crease with the IGAP. Before the operation we often look for the perforators using MRI, CT or duplex scans, which make these flaps much more reliable.

Very occasionally at operation we find that the perforator vessels are not as good as we hoped, and sometimes we have to fall back on the TRAM flap. Some surgeons always do a free TRAM rather than a DIEP flap.

In the **free microsurgical TRAM flap**, some muscle as well as skin and fat from the abdomen is transplanted into the breast area. The muscle is necessary as a carrier for the blood supply. Again there is usually enough tissue to build a breast without the use of an implant when removing the tissue from the abdomen area. The abdomen is tightened as in a 'tummy tuck'.

This is also a major procedure requiring several hours of surgery and six or so days in hospital. Here, because muscle is taken away, a mesh is usually applied to reinforce the abdomen in order to prevent the occurrence of weakness and hernia. There is still a reported 10% chance of this occurring.

Very occasionally, if the blood supply is precarious we have to use the **PEDICLED TRAM FLAP**, where even more rectus muscle (one of the 'crunch' muscles) is taken. This does not require microsurgery as the blood supply is still connected at the top, but a large mesh is required since weakness and hernias are more common. The operation lasts about 3-4 hours, with a 5 day stay in hospital. This flap is less reliable, and a smaller breast is usually produced.

The **TUG FLAP** is a new flap where a small muscle is taken along with skin and fat from the upper inner thigh. It is useful for slim patients who do not have enough tissue on the abdomen for a DIEP flap and who do not want their buttocks used. It produces a good B cup breast. There may be prolonged leakage from the thigh wounds, so bandaging of the leg is recommended.

All these autologous (where your own tissue only is used) techniques have been remarkably successful at producing a natural and permanent reconstruction. You also benefit by a flatter, smoother contour of the abdomen and hips or a more youthful buttock.

If there is little fat on the abdomen, the buttock flaps are used to make a breast. Patients who are obese, diabetic or smokers are not usually good candidates for microsurgical autologous breast reconstruction.

What happens to the nipple?

A nipple completes the reconstruction of a breast.

Silicone stick-on nipple and areolas may be selected, and they are held in place by glue or gel.

They are custom-made from a template of the normal side.

The nipple can also be reconstructed. It can be made with local tissue from the breast reconstruction, by taking part of the remaining nipple and 'sharing' it, or by using labia or earlobe. This may or may not be done at the initial reconstruction of the breast, according to the surgeon's preference. Usually it will be done at the same time in the case of an immediate reconstruction. With a delayed reconstruction the nipple is created later in order to allow for more accurate positioning on the reconstructed breast as the shape of the reconstructed breast changes in the early months as it matures.

The areola is tattooed soon after or sometimes formed from a skin graft.

What about the other breast?

With many reconstructions the new breast does not necessarily match the size and shape of the remaining natural breast. Consequently the other breast may be made bigger or smaller as well to match. If you have a particularly large or droopy breast on the other side, or if you feel it is too small, why not use this opportunity to get it changed if you have always wanted to?

Lipofilling/ lipomodelling may also be used to augment either of the breasts.

Post operative tips

Prepare yourself before your surgery. If you can, eat healthily, get as fit as possible, stop smoking in order to get through the surgery as well as possible. Make sure that you can rest for a good two weeks afterwards and have someone to look after you.

Scars take between a year and two years to mature, depending on your skin type. This does not mean that the wounds have not healed. Scars change as time go on: for the first two weeks they are very fine; then for about six weeks they become thick and red and often itch; everything feels tight and you may get little electric shocks as the nerves try to grow back. After that the scars soften gradually but remain red until fully mature.

Scars can also become very thick, unsightly and itchy: they are called hypertrophic. Massage and taping appears to reduce the chance of this happening.

Listen to your body. Do not try to do too much or feel that you should be fully recovered in a couple of weeks. I often advise patients to have a little siesta or rest every 3 to 4 hours in the first month.

It is useful to have a couple of contacts: a nurse and an ex-patient who can advise or reassure you during your recovery if you are worried, and make you feel less alone. Or maybe just for a laugh.

What happens if there are complications?

I must mention complications because you need to know what they are in order to decide which reconstruction is the right one for you.

There are specific complications relating to each of the methods used. Even the simplest operation with an implant can be complicated by infection, rejection of the implant and progressive firmness of the scar capsule around the reconstructed breast. A thick capsule may distort the appearance and even be painful. You are likely to develop a significant capsule following radiotherapy, and some surgeons including myself avoid implants if radiotherapy is planned. All these complications require further surgery.

Flaps can cause problems at their donor sites (from where the flap is taken) such as seroma fluid collection of the back with the latissimus dorsi flap. Weakness and hernias of the abdomen occur more commonly with the TRAM flap, because muscle is lifted with the flap, than with the DIEP flap. The main complication is loss of the flap if the flap does not have enough blood supply. If this happens you can have another reconstruction later, but you will need to wait for your body to recover.

As I have said before, careful selection of the right technique for the right patient by the right surgeon helps to reduce the potential complication rate.

Conclusion

Breast reconstruction has become an important part of the treatment of breast cancer. Most women who undergo reconstruction feel completely 'whole' and highly recommend it to other women faced with losing a breast.

New implants are continually being developed and more should be available in the next five years. Alternatively, autologous reconstruction has evolved into a reliable and safe method to achieve a natural, permanent reconstructed breast.

It is important to reiterate that you should not feel pressured into having a breast reconstruction. You should be fully informed and, under guidance, allowed to decide for yourself which option is the best for you. You must be told about the full range of breast reconstructions, not just offered the one operation. After all, it is the one time in the whole terrible process of cancer that you get to have a say. So use this opportunity.

GLOSSARY

Areola: pink bit around the nipple

Autologous: using your own body tissue (skin, fat, muscle) and no implant

Bilateral: both sides

Capsule: thick scar tissue around an implant, which can deform it. Cause unknown

Chemotherapy: drug treatment to kill cancer cells

Delayed reconstruction: reconstruction at a later time than the mastectomy.

Excision: surgery to cut out something

Expander: empty balloon placed under the skin which is slowly blown up to stretch the skin

Extrusion: the implant is seen through the skin and is rejected

Flap: piece of tissue which is moved

Free flap: piece of tissue which is detached before moving, and then sewn under microscope

Types of flaps:

flaps containing muscle are named after the muscle:

TRAM: transverse rectus abdominis muscle from abdomen

Latissimus dorsi: latissimus dorsi muscle from back

TUG: transverse upper gracilis muscle from upper inner thigh

perforator flaps only contain skin and fat and are named after their artery:

DIEP: deep inferior epigastric perforator from abdomen

SIEA: superficial inferior epigastric artery from abdomen

IGAP: inferior gluteal artery perforator from buttock crease

SGAP: superior gluteal artery perforator from upper buttock

Hernia: weakness in the abdomen through which the innards can push

Immediate reconstruction: at the same time as the mastectomy

Implant: foreign body, e.g. breast implant

Lipofilling/lipomodelling: taking fat, concentrating it and reinjecting it to fill defects

Lumpectomy: operation to remove a breast lump

Mastectomy: surgical removal of a breast

Mastopexy: breast lift

Microsurgery: surgery where a microscope is used, often to reattach blood vessels

Radiotherapy: X-ray treatment to kill cancer cells

Seroma: collection of fluid in a cavity. Can cause discomfort or get infected

Silicone: a substance derived from silicon, a naturally occurring element found in sand and rock and chemically altered for its use in breast implants

BREAST RECONSTRUCTION AFTER MASTECTOMY SUMMARY

Implant used
- <u>Implant alone</u> (often after tissue expansion)
- <u>Expander/Implant + latissimus dorsi flap from the back</u>

No implant used
- <u>Back</u> — Extended latissimus dorsi
- <u>Abdomen</u>
  - Pedicled TRAM
  - Free TRAM
  - Free Perforator Flap: DIEP/SIEA/PUP
- <u>Buttock</u> — Free Perforator Flap: IGAP/SGAP
- <u>Other</u> — TUG

Other breast
- <u>Augmentation</u>
- <u>Reduction</u>
- <u>Mastopexy</u>

USEFUL INFORMATION SITES

GREAT BRITAIN

The British Association of Plastic, Reconstructive and Aesthetic Surgeons
Royal College of Surgeons
35-43 Lincoln's Inn Fields
London WC2A 3PE
Telephone: 020 7831 5161
Website: www.bapras.org.uk

Breakthrough Breast Cancer
3rd Floor, Weston House
246, High Holborn
London WC1V 7EX
Telephone: 08080 100 200
Website: www.breakthroughbreastcancer.org.uk
Breakthrough Breast Cancer is a charity dedicated to funding research, promoting awareness and campaigning to improve Breast Cancer services.

Breast Cancer Care
Kiln House
210 New Kings Road
London SW6 4NZ
Helpline: 0808 800 6000
Website: www.breastcancercare.org.uk

Breast Cancer Care provides breast cancer information and support across the UK. All - services are free and include a helpline, website, publications and practical and emotional support. They have specific support for partners and for younger women affected by breast cancer.

Breast Cancer Care (Scotland)
4th Floor, 40 St Enoch Square
Glasgow G1 4DH
Telephone: 0845 0771 892
Website: www.breastcancercare.org.uk

Breast Cancer Support Board
A UK based internet message board for women with breast cancer. Run by 6 women with experience of breast cancer, this network offers support and advice and welcomes newcomers.
Website: www.breastcancersupport.co.uk/

Cancerbackup
3 Bath Place
Rivington Street
London EC2A 3JR
Telephone: 0808 800 1234
Website: www.cancerbackup.org.uk

Cancerbackup Scotland
3rd floor, Cranston House
104-114 Argyle Street
Glasgow G2 8BH
Telephone: 0141 223 7676
Cancerbackup – the British Association of Cancer
    United Patients. This charity was founded by Dr
    Vicky Clement-Jones after her own experiences
    with cancer. Cancerbackup offers information,
    advice and emotional support to cancer patients
    and their families. It has publications about the
    main types of cancer, treatments and ways of
    living with cancer. Cancerbackup also produce a
    newsletter, Cancerbackup News.

Cancer Research UK
P.O. Box 123
London WC2A 3PX
Admin telephone number: 020 7242 0200
CancerHelp UK is one of Cancer Research UK's 5
    main websites. You can access all these
    websites on www.cancerresearchuk.org

Hereditary Breast Cancer Helpline
Telephone: 01629 813000 (helpline 24 hours)
Email: canhelp@btopenworld.com
This organisation provides support and information
to anyone concerned about hereditary breast
cancer. There is usually someone to answer calls
during office hours. If not, there is a 24 hour
answerphone. Leave your number and someone
will call you back.

Irish Cancer Society
43/45 Northumberland Road
Dublin 4
Ireland
Telephone: 01231 0500
Website: www.webmaster@irishcancer.ie

Look Good Feel Better
Albany House
Claremont Lane
Esher
Surrey KT10 9DA
Telephone: 01372 470900,
Fax: 01372 470959
E-mail: info@lookgoodfeelbetter.co.uk
Website: www.lookgoodfeelbetter.co.uk
A charity set up by the cosmetics industry,
    volunteer beauty therapists provide skincare
    and make up workshops for women undergoing
    cancer treatment. All guests are provided with a
    goodie bag worth £150–£200. It has been

running for 12 years and workshops are held in 40 hospitals across the UK. Find your nearest workshop and read more about the work of the charity on their website.

Useful websites

www.breakthrough.org.uk
www.optionsforbreastreconstruction.com
www.diepflap.com
Department of Health website:
   www.dh.gov.uk

CANADA

The Canadian Society of Plastic Surgeons
 Joseph Blvd. E. #4 1469
Montreal, QC Canada H2J 1M6
Telephone: 514-843-5415; Fax: 514-843-7005
www.plasticsurgery.ca
www.breastofcanada.com/

AUSTRALIA

Breast Cancer Network Australia
293 Camberwell Rd
Camberwell
Victoria
Australia 3124
E-mail: beacon@bcna.org.au
Telephone: (03) 9805 2500

National Breast Cancer Center
92 Parramatta Road
Camperdown NSW 2050
Australia
E-mail: directorate@nbcc.org.au
Telephone: (2) 9036 3030

INDEX OF OPERATIONS

 Barbara 53 Right delayed DIEP flap (+left mastopexy) 1 year ago.
Nipple by nipple sharing

 Lynda 53 Right delayed DIEP flap (+left breast reduction) 4 months ago.
Nipple from right earlobe 3 weeks ago

 Mel 45 Right delayed bilateral differential implants 8 months ago

 Bronwen 52 Bilateral delayed DIEP flaps 1 year ago.
No nipples

 Christine 61 Left immediate free TRAM 7 years ago.
Nipple by nipple sharing

 Katherine 58 Bilateral immediate Becker expander/implants 2 years ago.
Nipples from labia

 Jackie 50 Left immediate DIEP flap 2 years ago.
Nipple by nipple sharing

 Judith 58 Right immediate free TRAM flap 3 years ago (+left augmentation mastopexy).
Nipple by local tissue

 Susan 57 Left delayed latissimus dorsi (+ right reduction) 3 years ago.
Nipple with local flap

 Liz 50 Right immediate reconstruction with 2 IGAP flaps 2½ years ago.
Nipple from local flap

 Lyndsey 52 Left immediate DIEP flap 1½ years ago. Lipofilling to increase projection.
Nipple by nipple sharing

 Pat 60 Left immediate DIEP flap (+ right reduction) 1½ years ago.
Nipple from local tissue

Pearl 68 Left immediate free TRAM flap 8 years ago.
Nipple by local tissue

 Shirley 55 Right delayed latissimus dorsi flap 2½ years ago.
Nipple by nipple sharing

 Stella 72 Bilateral delayed DIEP flap 1 year and 2 years ago.
Nipples from local tissue

 Sue 47 Left immediate IGAP flap 2 years ago. Lipofilling. (+ Right mastopexy).
Nipple by nipple sharing

 Chic Left delayed implant (+ right mastopexy and implant) 2 years ago.
Nipple by nipple sharing

 Emma 34 Left immediate implant 3 years ago. Right immediate implant 2 years ago.
Left nipple by nipple sharing

 Debbie 49 Right delayed SIEA flap 2 years ago.
Nipple from labia

 Mary 64 Right delayed implant (+ left augmentation) 4 months ago. Tattoo.
No nipple

 Gill 43 Left delayed DIEP flap 2 years ago.
Nipple by nipple sharing

 Chrystèle 35 Right delayed IGAP flap 1½ year ago.
Nipple from labia

 Suzy 34 Left delayed DIEP flap 2 years ago.
Nipple with local flap

AUTHOR AND CONTRIBUTORS

Elaine Sassoon

Elaine is a Consultant Plastic Surgeon and head of the Department of Plastic Surgery at the Norfolk and Norwich University Hospital in Norwich, England. Her main subspecialty is breast surgery and reconstruction, with a particular interest in microsurgery and perforator flaps. She was educated at Harvard University, USA and attended Medical School at University College Hospital in London before training in England and spending overseas attachments in Ljubljana, Atlanta, Taipei and New Orleans. She is chairman of the Breast Special Interest Group of the British Association of Plastic, Reconstructive and Aesthetic Surgeons, the Plastic Surgery representative on NICE for early breast cancer and runs several courses for nurses and plastic surgery trainees. She has been awarded numerous prizes both nationally and internationally.

'I have been thinking about this book for three years, and breathing it for six months. It has been really exciting and a rather moving experience. I hope that it does some good and that the result is as beautiful as the women in it.'

www.elainesassoon.com

Andrea O'Hare

Andrea is a renowned portrait photographer based in Londonderry, Northern Ireland. She has won several prestigious awards including Fuji Portrait Photographer of the Year twice; Northern Ireland Portrait Photographer of the Year; Fuji Wedding Photographer of the Year, and Avant-garde Wedding Photographer of the Year, 2007. She has lectured for Fuji and both the Irish and Northern Ireland Photographic Associations.

'I was truly delighted to be asked to take the photographs for this book of extraordinary women. I myself am a fellow breast cancer survivor and patient of Elaine, so even before I took the first photograph, I felt enormous empathy with them.

'With great locations and beautiful women (whose confidence was fuelled with a little bubbly), we were able to complete this shoot in only four days. I am very pleased with the results and every one of the girls should feel proud of their achievement. It has been a privilege to be part of the Boudica Project.'

derry@studio22photography.co.uk

Chrystèle Ganivet

As soon as Elaine mentioned her idea of this book Chrystèle offered her help and time. She edited the stories and with her unstinting energy helped to make the book reality. As she says herself, she instantly saw its potential value to women going through breast cancer.

'When I was faced with making a choice myself, the only images that I was shown were either line drawings or post-operative photos, which were scary in themselves! None of these came even remotely close to showing what a finished, reconstructed breast looked like. Breast reconstruction is not just a cosmetic procedure. It is an essential element for many women in re-discovering themselves, both physically and mentally following breast cancer. I wish that this was better understood by everyone.

'I became passionate about the book and began to push Elaine to move forward with it. The Boudica Project has been a great experience and an emotional journey, which has enriched my life considerably.'

Neil Watson

Neil is married to Chrystèle and initially got dragged along in the wake with her enthusiasm for the Boudica Project. He helped Chrystèle, photographed the shoot and took the pictures of Mary.

'I certainly saw the value of the book from a masculine perspective. It is true to say that breast cancer within a couple leaves two victims not one. Men also need to be reassured about their partner's physical and emotional wellbeing. This is a story that remains to be told.

'At the photo-shoot I documented the events in monochrome. I have to add that watching Andrea work has been both educational and inspirational. Meeting many of the women and editing their narratives has been moving. "The Boudica Within" is a truly inspired title for this book.'